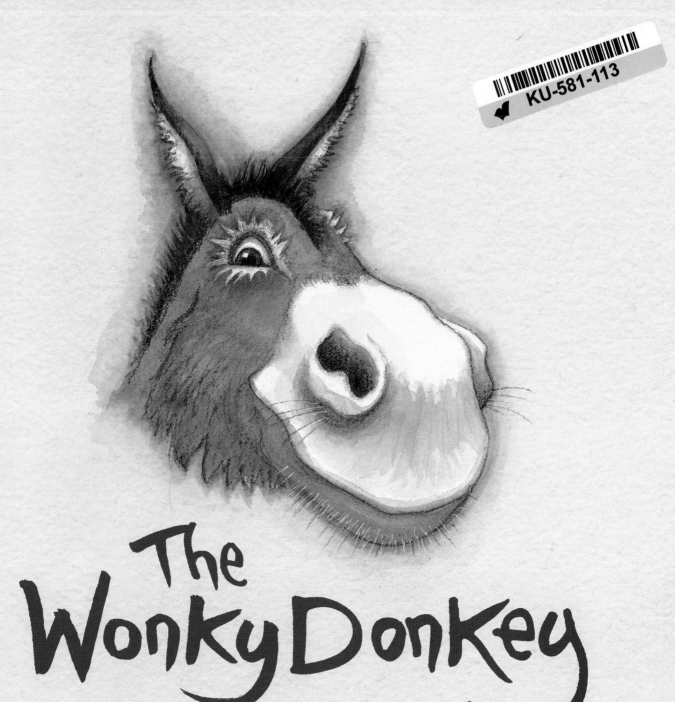

The Wonky Donkey

Words by **Craig Smith**

Illustrations by **Katz Cowley**

■ SCHOLASTIC

I was walking down the road
and I saw ...

We hope you enjoy this book.
Please return or renew it by the due date.
You can renew it at **www.norfolk.gov.uk/libraries**
or by using our free library app. Otherwise you can
phone **0344 800 8020** - please have your library
card and pin ready.
You can sign up for email reminders too.

For my mum,
and all the people who have helped me
over the years: family, friends and mentors.
Thank you.
– Craig Smith

To my precious Mum, Dad and aunt Wren …
your love, support and inspiration fuels my creative journey
and makes all of me smile and sing. With big-fat gratitude
for keeping me tuned to the magic and humour of life.
– Katz Cowley

First published in the UK by Scholastic, 2018
This edition published 2022
1 London Bridge, London, SE1 9BA
Scholastic Ireland, 89E Lagan Road, Dublin Industrial Estate, Glasnevin, Dublin, D11 HP5F

SCHOLASTIC and associated logos are trademarks and/or
registered trademarks of Scholastic Inc.

First published in New Zealand by Scholastic New Zealand Limited, 2009

Text © Craig Smith, 2007
Illustrations © Katz Cowley, 2009

The right of Craig Smith and Katz Cowley to be identified as the author and illustrator of this work
has been asserted by them under the Copyright, Designs and Patents Act 1988.

ISBN 978 0702 32368 3

A CIP catalogue record for this book is available from the British Library.

Printed in Italy
Paper made from wood grown in sustainable forests and other controlled sources.

1 3 5 7 9 10 8 6 4 2

www.scholastic.co.uk

a donkey,

Hee Haw)!

And he only had three legs!

He was a
wonky donkey.

I was walking down the road
and I saw a donkey,

He only had three legs ...

and one eye!

He was a **winky** wonky donkey.

I was walking down the road
and I saw a donkey,

Hee Haw!

He only had three legs,
one eye ...

and he liked to listen to country music.

Yee Haa!

He was a honky-tonky
winky wonky donkey.

I was walking down the road
and I saw a donkey,

Hee Haw!

He only had three legs,
one eye,
he liked to listen to country music ...

and he was quite tall and slim.

He was
a **lanky**
honky-
tonky
winky
wonky
donkey.

I was walking down the road
and I saw a donkey,

Hee Haw!

He only had three legs,
one eye,
he liked to listen to country music,
he was quite tall and slim ...

and he smelt really, really bad.

He was a **stinky-dinky** lanky honky-tonky winky wonky donkey.

I was walking down the road
and I saw a donkey,

Hee Haw!

He only had three legs,
one eye,
he liked to listen to country music,
he was quite tall and slim,
he smelt really, really bad ...

**and that morning he'd got up early
and hadn't had any coffee.**

He was a **cranky**
stinky-dinky lanky
honky-tonky
winky wonky donkey.

I was walking down the road
and I saw a donkey,

Hee Haw!

He only had three legs,

one eye,

he liked to listen to country music,

he was quite tall and slim,

he smelt really, really bad,

that morning he'd got up early

and hadn't had any coffee ...

and he was always getting up to mischief.

He was a **hanky-panky** cranky stinky-dinky lanky honky-tonky winky wonky donkey.

I was walking down the road
and I saw a donkey,

Hee Haw!

He only had three legs,
one eye,
he liked to listen to country music,
he was quite tall and slim,
he smelt really, really bad,
that morning he'd got up early
and hadn't had any coffee,
he was always getting up to mischief ...

but he was quite good looking!

He was a **spunky** hanky-panky cranky
stinky-dinky lanky honky-tonky winky wonky donkey!

I was walking down the road

and I saw a donkey ...

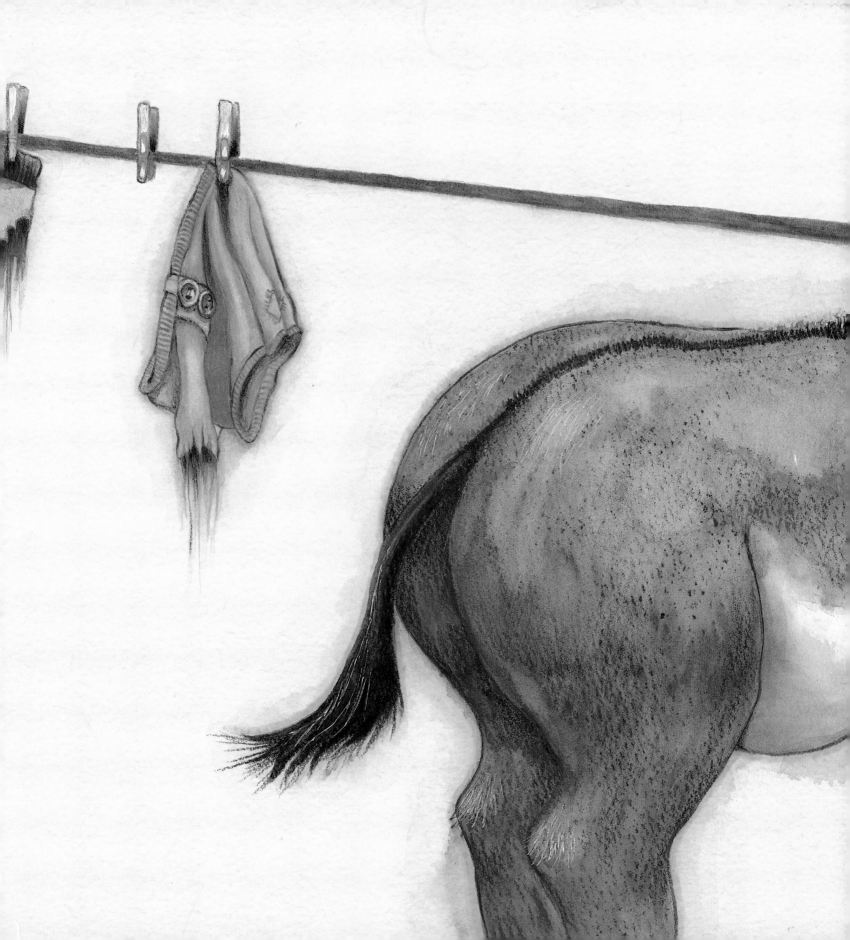